P

This

Michael Rosen was born in Harrow in 1946. He studied Medicine and English at university and has been writing, broadcasting and lecturing since the early seventies. He lives in Dalston, London.

This Is Not My Nose

MICHAEL ROSEN

PENGUIN BOOKS

PENGUIN BOOKS

Published by the Penguin Group
Penguin Books Ltd, 80 Strand, London WC2R 0RL, England
Penguin Putnam Inc., 375 Hudson Street, New York, New York 10014, USA
Penguin Books Australia Ltd, 250 Camberwell Road, Camberwell, Victoria 3124, Australia
Penguin Books Canada Ltd, 10 Alcorn Avenue, Toronto, Ontario, Canada M4V 3B2
Penguin Books India (P) Ltd, 11 Community Centre, Panchsheel Park, New Delhi – 110 017, India
Penguin Books (NZ) Ltd, Cnr Rosedale and Airborne Roads, Albany, Auckland, New Zealand
Penguin Books (South Africa) (Pty) Ltd, 24 Sturdee Avenue, Rosebank 2196, South Africa

Penguin Books Ltd, Registered Offices: 80 Strand, London WC2R 0RL, England

www.penguin.com

Published in Penguin Books 2004
1

Set in 10.5/14.75 pt Linotype Minion
Typeset by Rowland Phototypesetting Ltd, Bury St Edmunds, Suffolk
Printed in England by Clays Ltd, St Ives plc

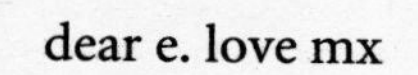
dear e. love mx

'. . . nor this is not my nose, neither. Nothing that is so, is so.'

(Feste in *Twelfth Night,* Act IV, scene i)

My friends in the suburbs didn't know that on Sundays I travelled across London and walked by rows of terrace houses, greyed with years of coal fires. They didn't know that in one of these houses was a Bubbe in a purple cardigan, a Zeyde in a suit and an Uncle eating chopped herring. I didn't speak of the lav that was outside, damp and dangerous but though I could never understand how the ship got into the bottle on the mantelpiece, that was something I could mention. My mother and father in a picture on the wall too, standing in long coats in a doorway, arm in arm, younger than how I knew them, she with a perm, he with a chunk of a plaster on his leg. But what of the walks to the Bag Laundry with Bubbe kvetshing about how uncle Ronnie was cheated, she was cheated, I was cheated? Or Zeyde taking me to Hackney Downs, where men in dark blue suits like his stood around in a group? Say nothing. Say nothing at all. That wide flat open green, rimmed in the distance with the sooty terraces, and the men in suits standing talking, but not in English.

In between one of our long spells of cricket
in the back yard, Keith, whose Dad was a
butcher, asked me who I thought did the
most important job? He said that he thought
it was probably the men who make electricity.
Without electricity, where would we be? he said.
I, whose Dad was an English teacher, said that
I thought the most important job in the world
was being an English teacher.

The upper levels of the Science Museum were rigged for people wanting to get good A-levels. Lenses and particles. But no one was there apart from me and my brother. A difficult, empty place. He took me to Sound and we stood in a booth and listened. It's about Harmonics, he said. You listen. I put the earphones on. A flat male voice is repeating with no pause or break or ups or downs: '. . . home steve williams coming home steve williams coming home steve williams coming . . .' It never stops or starts. It just talks forever. It's there when I put the cans on, it's still going on when I put the cans down. We walk round the upper levels, along the empty aisles, past the cases full of equipment and apparatus, squeaking our feet on the lino, trying it ourselves: '. . . home steve williams coming home steve williams coming . . .' On the way back on the Tube, we pick different points to start and finish: '. . . coming home steve williams coming home steve williams.' Or: '. . . williams coming home steve williams coming home steve.'

I stayed in the headteacher's house next door to his school in Issy-les-Moulineaux. Their oldest son wore military uniform and, as they often told me, went to the Ecole Polytechnique. Once when we were out, a man coming down the path towards us saluted him, and his mother was excited. On the same path the next day I learnt the word for dog shit, because she got excited that one of us younger ones might tread in it. They found me some English books. We spent a long, long time looking at Napoleon's tomb but when we went to the Eiffel Tower, there were long queues so I read *An Inspector Calls* and wondered about why she swallowed disinfectant. I had a feeling it was my fault.

Malc's shoes smelled of fish because they
had been stuck together with fish glue. His
father had brought them back from Czechoslovakia.
They were, his father said, another
example of how Communism was improving
the lives of the Czechoslovakian people.
– See how resourceful they are, he said, using
fish remains to make shoes. Nothing gets
wasted.

At nights, when we lay in his bedroom – Malc in his
bed, me on the floor in my sleeping bag – we would
talk about the girls we fancied; and in the dark
I could smell his Communist shoes.

When *Lady Chatterley* came out, the kid we
called Tails brought one in. He covered
it in brown paper and wrote on the front: *Black
Beauty* by Anna Sewell. In class, we'd say,
What are you reading, Tails? And he'd say: *Black
Beauty*. We'd say, What's *Black Beauty* like,
Tails? Good book, he'd say. That year, we all read
Black Beauty.

For a year they taught us Clause Analysis. Our teacher gave us an infallible guide: a Table of Subordinate Clauses, each one introduced by a header word. There was the Adverbial Clause of Time, introduced by 'when'. There were Adverbial Clauses of Concession and Condition, introduced by 'though', 'although', 'if', I've forgotten the rest. But the thing that was important was the table. Learn the table and we were in the clear. Week after week we did lessons and homework on Clause Analysis and the table was there to help us. Then came the O-level exam in English Language and our teacher told us that we should turn first to the section on Clause Analysis so we could get that out of the way right from the start. I did. The passage was bristling with clauses. Right in the middle of it, was a clause that began 'no matter how . . .' What? 'No matter how . . .' wasn't on the table. I had never seen 'no matter how . . .' in one of our lessons or homeworks. What was it an Adverbial Clause of? Maybe it was an Adverbial Clause of something she hadn't told us about. I reckoned that the examiners knew the table she used and went off and found a clause that wasn't on it.

We had thumbed lifts as far south as Montauban. Stoll said he wanted to see the house where Ingres lived. After that, Albi and Toulouse-Lautrec's place. Very different kinds of flesh. The skin on Ingres' posh women looks like grapes. Lautrec's prostitutes, white and purple in and out the shadows. Not that I could compare it in any great detail with the real thing. Stoll, though, had drawn himself in bed with someone called Anna listening to Charlie Parker. I thought Montauban was worth a stop. The French guy who came in for our A-level orals gave us his address there. M. Vitse. He said that France would never give up Algeria and slung his jacket over his shoulders without putting his arms through the sleeves. He taught us the song that Jeanne Moreau sings in *Jules et Jim*.

– Come, he said. *N'importe quand*. Come see me in Montauban.

When we called on his house, he looked us up and down. You could see the panic.

– The house is full, he said. *Les amis, les parents.*
– No, no, I said, we just came to see you. It wasn't to stay. *Pour dire bonjour*.

He shut the door.
– Fascist.
– Yeah.
We went on to Albi. Lautrec was closed for repairs and we split up somewhere near Perpignan. 35 years later, I heard that a woman turned up on Stoll's doorstep and said that he was her father and her mother was someone called Anna.

Marching across the Park to school, saluting
Sixth Formers, his moustache at the ready,
he had a special pocket inside the jacket of his
suit where he kept a tennis shoe to belt boys with.
You couldn't see it, but everyone knew it was there,
and sometimes on a quiet day, you might be head
down, a door slammed, a brief shout, the sound of
the tennis shoe hitting a boy's body, another slam
and it was a quiet day again. You couldn't even see
the outline of it against his suit.

– *Antony and Cleopatra*. You know, chaps, Antony
was a military man, a man that men would lie
down and die for. I once knew someone like that.
I was in the Officers' Training Corps in 1933 and
the Prince of Wales, later to become King Edward,
came to review us. And do you know, every man
jack of us would have been willing to lie down and
die for him. That was Antony. These are the kinds
of things we can chat about now that you're in the
Sixth Form. Carry on.

After I was taken out of the apparatus that was
supposed to be pulling me back together
they sent me to the Garston Rehabilitation Centre
where I was given a navy blue track-suit. By
then I could walk, which was more than Johnny
could. He was fixing a light on the roof of
a factory when the scaffold tower he was
standing on began to fall. He jumped up and
grabbed the girder above his head and the tower
fell to the ground. He hung from the girder
while the others went to find a ladder but they
couldn't find one long enough, so they rang for
the fire brigade and stood down below shouting
at him, telling him to hang on. The drop smashed
his feet and legs in ways that I didn't want to look
at when he showed me. He slid about on crutches,
pushing his fat shoes on the lino. And at Tea-and-biscuits,
when we sat in our track-suits round
green felt tables, he told us how he did it with
his girlfriend when he went home at weekends.
For this, he was warned about language. 'Language,
Johnny, language.'

I went out on the playing-field and tried to remember how to run. I could walk and I could jump, but that thing where you take off from one foot and land on the other and then you take off from the one that you just landed on and there's no break? That defeated me. It was like the way you don't know how the back of your head looks. I spent days doing the jumping from foot to foot thing.

In 1963 in one of the lifts on Goodge Street
Station there was an ad for Jaeger cardigans.
There was a man and a woman in a loose clinch.
They were looking into each other's eyes.
I thought it would feel good to have love
like that. That you could look right into each
other's eyes. That would be good. Underneath,
it said, 'We're in love with Jaeger.'

1)

I told them that it felt like lead. Yesterday
I had run along a stretch of the North
Circular faster than the traffic but today
it was like lead. Tomorrow I won't go to
the North Circular.

Her mother had a dog. A tiny hairless thing that quivered, a penis that barked. One ring on the door and it jumped out of its basket into the hallway. There, on the lino, it lost its grip and it ski-ed on its toenails till it hit the door. Her mother ran out and lifted it up, folding her arms round its naked body. It crouched there, panting; while she rubbed noses with it saying boo boo boo.

2)

Jim sat on the bus in his shirt. I sat on the bus in a shirt and a jumper and a jacket. He said he was fine. He said he wasn't cold. I was cold. I was cold like when your ribs go stiff.

The buzzer rang and it was Robert, the Allen Ginsberg lookalike. Robert the radical Ranter, the living-theatre man, the drunk. He asked to come up and he sat at my gate-legged table. He was anxious and asked me, did I think he was real? Did I believe all that Ginsberg stuff he did? Yes, I did believe it. He did what I would have liked to have done. He shouted poems on street corners and at sit-ins. He invented plays in rooms with low ceilings. He was a happening.

– It was all fake, he said. It was all a fake. I was pretending. I was working for B.O.S.S. I had to spy on South Africans over here and tell B.O.S.S. if they were involved in anything. It's why I was drunk. It's to do with my parents in South Africa. I was in debt, incredible debt, and there was no way I could tell them.

– I said, you'd better go.

3)

I used to be able to beat an egg. Odd: five or six beats and my arm seizes up.

Two men came and sat in my kitchen,
opened their suitcases on the table,
took out files and plastic folders and
asked me if I knew anyone who might be
able to front a show they were producing.
I suggested Alex, musician, story-teller,
writer, entertainer . . . (they seemed interested) . . .
. . . and presenter of a radio programme called
Black Londoners.
He's black, is he? said one of the men.
Yes, I said.
Does he try to bring it in? he asked.
What? I said.
Being black, he said, being black. Does he
try to bring it in?

4)

For this class they did registration in a
Chemistry lab and one girl said that I
was on drugs. Your speech is slurred,
she said, and you're slow, you're so
slow. What are you on? You must be
on something. I said, I'm not on anything,
I don't do that. And I wasn't and I
didn't. I'd never touched anything.
Then she said, and you're so white.
She was black.

He said that the thing that got them sent down was the photos. He had them there. A building site, pickets, Des Warren and Ricky Tomlinson talking. Broken windows.
– You see, he said, that was the order they showed them in court.

We were on the back seat of a coach going to the TUC conference. He would show people that they shouldn't be in the nick.
– The windows was broken before Dezzy and Ricky got there. It's as simple as that. But that prat of a lawyer didn't say that in court. It would have got them off . . .
He shuffled the photos.
– See, it tells a different story.

5)

You need to slim down your fingers, he said. If you're going to edit film you need slim fingers. You're going to have to slim down those fingers.

In a cartoon, at a time when some government or
other was pleading with us to tighten our belts
or go to war, or both, an overseer stood over a
shipful of galley-slaves with a whip in his hand
urging them on with: 'We're all in the same boat.'
A bit like when the Lone Ranger turned to Tonto,
his faithful companion from the Powatomie Nation,
and the Lone Ranger says, 'Hey, Tonto, we're
surrounded by Indians.' And Tonto says, 'How do
you mean, "we", kemosabe?'

6)

There was something about my hair. Sometimes after rain the ends used to curl up. Now it was like wire wool.

The most successful amongst us was
Jones, sad-dog eyes and a full-length
leather coat. He had been all over Vietnam
and his pix were in a fat book. He was
here, he said, to learn how to be a film-maker.
He got on the van at Holland Park
with a woman from Yorkshire who said
that I was a bourgeois opportunist and
we were taken to a place that looked like
a second world war prisoner-of-war camp.
Now it was a film school. After a few
months in the huts, he took an Arriflex and
his Yorkshire friend to his home town in
South Wales and shot miles of film. He
brought it back and chopped it into strips
and hung them up with their tails dangling
into canvas-lined bins. You could look in
through the Crittall-windows and see them:
hundreds of trails running down from their
steel hooks into the bins. After three years,
we finished there. I think he left it all in the
hut.

7)

Yes, I'll have a cup of tea, you said, and then I'm off. And I said, I've just got to hang out the washing. And you never got your cup of tea. I just went on hanging out the washing. Just a shirt and trousers. It just went on and on. First the shirt and then the trousers. Longer than it takes to make tea and drink it.

I sat in the Bird Gallery. Above my head stuffed swallows seemed to fly across the sky. In one case, a painted farm with a real gutter and eaves housed a martins' nest, built from their gobfuls of mud. In another, hedgerow birds mobbed an owl, their beaks wide open, caught in the act of making its life a misery.

If I meet friends I haven't seen for twenty years, I'm surprised to find that they haven't stayed in a glass case, soundlessly screeching.

8)

It was the bit of the eyelid that the eyelash comes out of. Swollen. My eyelashes came out of sausages, something was in there, pressing against the skin, bloating it.

If you asked you could get to see the talc mine. It was a crater in the Pyrenees. The bulldozers and trucks down below were nearly too far to hear, so they crawled about humming. Nothing grew on the ledges and terraces all the way down. It's not only for ladies after they have had a shower, he said. It's used in making gramophone records. Mostly they're North Africans. Where do they live? Over there. There was a tin hut, like a tin railway carriage, with a row of iron beds inside and a stand-pipe outside.

9)

I couldn't catch the bus. I ran but couldn't run.

So I took him to the mother and toddler's group in the community centre and he played on the tractors and he ran round and round laughing. There were about six women and their kids. One said that when her old man comes home pissed she ties a knot in the bottom of his pyjama trousers and she listens to him in the dark hopping about trying to get his legs in. One said that it was a tragedy that Hess was still in jail in Germany. It was a crime that our government was keeping him in there and we should all do what we could to get him out before he died and he played on the tractors and ran round and round laughing.

10)

I listened to my voice on the tape: deep and slow. As if I was talking through a yawn.

They whacked him over the head and he died
but they didn't kill him. The court said
he had a thin skull, in which case I suppose
it was his fault, walking about with a fragile
head within easy reach of a truncheon. Anyway,
the court said, there were six of them so it
wasn't possible to say which one of them did
it, so they thought it best to say that none of
them did it.

I read something that I had written about it to a
class in a London school. I did know him, after
all. One boy said his dad was in the SPG (the same
brigade that had killed him), and it weren't like
that. Next day, the police liaison officer was up
at the school and I got a call from the head saying
that I had to go. The teachers at the school said
that I wasn't going (he had been a teacher, after all)
so the head changed his mind. As did the police, I
suppose.

11)

Just do one thing in a day. That's all I can do. One thing. Do that one thing ok and the day was ok.

I sat in a miner's terrace house with my tape machine and he said, in the voice of the Dulais Valley, automation never benefited us, it merely dispensed with our services. Remember, I go to work, to earn money, to buy bread, to build up my strength, to go to work, to earn money, to buy bread, to build up my strength. You see?

12)

Hours of sleep. Ten hours. Twelve hours. More sleep. I want more sleep. Let me lie here and sleep some more. Put me in a chair and I'll sleep. Leave me in bed and I'll sleep. Hours of sleep.

13)

Snow is the enemy. And frost. They come for me. They work their way into my blood. When I see them coming I barricade my body with Damart underwear and fleeces. I sleep in a cashmere jumper and double up on the gloves. With no loo in the house, a piss or shit is dangerous. Moving down the side of the house on the ice lets the cold get into my feet. Twisting out of the clothes lets the air roar in. Sitting on the pan is a surrender.

I was walking through Cricklewood, a cop on a bike stopped me and asked me if I was on the jury where that feller got off the charge of trying to steal a London bus. Yes, I said. That's the third time they've tried to get him for that, he said. You see, he's in the National Front, and he wants to get his PSV driving licence. So he hides on board the buses and when they shut up for the night, he drives a bus round the depot. But they never see him at it. They know he does it but they don't catch him. And they want him out of the bus station because he's a fascist. They bring charges but the case collapses because they can never agree where he's supposed to have driven the bus.

14)

I had to deal with my eyes. A slight touch of wind and they filled up with water and it poured on to my cheeks.

He said, if they don't like it in the North
they can go to the Republic. They've got
their own place to go to. He said he was one
of the reasonable ones, not like the hooligans
who play flutes and wear tattoos.

15)

I went to the doctor with my eyes and he said it was conjunctivitis. He gave me some yellow paste to squeeze into my eyes.

16)

You never used to look like Buddha, he said. That way you've got of just sitting there and smiling. Big and slow. Blinking slowly. I can't even tell when your eyes are open or closed. Weren't you, like, wild? Running all over the place?

17)

I told the doctor that the conjunctivitis cream hadn't worked. He said that he thought it might be kidneys.

It all came down to who owned the bikes.
We slept on the floor in the director's office
and in the morning they took us round the
factory to show us how they made them.
The line was still and half-finished bikes
were standing there. You might think
they had been parked there, but they were
too new and looking closely you could
see they were skeletons. They said that
the guy who had bought the factory was
just waiting to sell it off. A cowboy, they
said. And the bikes were sitting outside in the
yard. In wooden boxes, stacked high. The
steward who had spent his life asking for 2
and 3 and 4 per cent said that they had made
the bikes so now it was down to them to work
out what to do with them. We stood in the yard
and looked up at the stack. It seemed like this
was a brief time when we could think of them
in a new way.

18)

The kidney test showed that there was something going on. Not very much, but there was a slight reading on the haemoglobin which might be significant, he said. The best thing I could do was go to the Renal Department.

19)

At the Renal Department, he had my file in front of me. He asked me what I had been doing that week. I told him I had been making a Schools TV programme with kids from the Isle of Dogs. He said that he thought this stuff about my kidneys was rubbish and he pushed the file to one side. You're hypothyroid, he said. He started to get excited. I've got fifteen students with me today. I'm going to get them in to see if they know what's wrong with you. This is great. Don't tell them what I've said, OK? No, I won't, I said. OK, you lot, in you come, he said. Look at this. He was very excited. I was thinking about hypothyroid from my year at medical school fifteen years earlier. I remembered a page in Samson Wright's *Physiology*. A before and after. There was a woman with a round plump white face, like mine. Then next to it, a picture of the same woman. Her face was angular and bony, like mine had once been. When was that? Ten years ago? Twelve? I sat and waited for the students as the years ran over me, and my eyes watered even more.

20)

The students stood round me. It's his kidneys, sir. He's got renal failure, sir. What? he shouted. Kidneys? Just because we're on the Renal Unit here doesn't mean that he must necessarily have kidney failure. You haven't done the basics, have you? Pulse rate, reflexes, temperature. You haven't even felt his skin. Do you know, if you had done those four tests, you would know what he's got. Look at this. He bashed my knee with the rubber hammer. No reflex whatsoever. Feel this. He put his hand on my cheek. Cold and clammy, he said. Feel his pulse rate. Ridiculously low. And look at his eyelids. Have you ever seen eyelids like that? So what do you think he's got? Some kind of renal problem, sir? No, he's hypothyroid. Look at the myxoedema on his ankles. He's only 34, you know. Can you stand up, Mr Rosen? Will you please walk along the line of the carpet, putting one foot in front of another. I tried to walk along the line of the carpet, putting one foot in front of another. I couldn't.

21)

A week later I was back for the results of the blood test. This time I was with Dr Gesundheit from New York. Is your name really Gesundheit? I said. Yes, he said. Where did you get it from? I got it at about the same time as I got my genes, he said. Now let's look at your results. He turned the page over. Technically you're dead, he said. And if you're not dead, you should be in a torpor. They shouldn't have sent you home last week. Not only are you not producing any thyroxine, but the antibodies that destroyed your thyroid aren't there either. You're running on no thyroid, like a car running on no gas. You have to come in now. Right now. I'm going to order you a bed in the Metabolic Unit.

22)

I was in a room with Charlie. His tongue
was too big to fit in his mouth. And in the
corner was a kid. I thought it was a kid.
It turned out he was a man but he was still
a kid. There was a group area with the TV
and there was a man who barked. Dog man.
He was seven foot tall and his head hung
down on his chest, his arms hung low,
right down by his side. There was ball lady.
She was completely round. Really two balls.
One round bald head, on a round body, no
neck. You look bad, they said to me. You
look like a corpse. You sound like it too,
they said. You sound like you're talking
from underground. And you're cold like
a corpse too. You're the Dead Man, man.

23)

Every day they brought a sheet of white paper with a heap of white powder on it. I had to eat it. And a couple of hours later I had to go off and have tests. You won't believe what's happening to you, said the doctor. You're going to change so much, so fast. He loved that. He threw his head back and laughed.

24)

I emerged. An old me came out of the Dead Man. Every day, I saw the face and hands and ankles shrink. I heard my voice speed up and rise. My lips shrank. I could move my tongue quicker and I unfroze. After ten years of being cold I wasn't cold any more. Charlie and Dog Man and Ball Lady and the kid who wasn't a kid were excited. It's all so quick, they said.

25)

I used to be too old to walk up hills. I couldn't carry a box of books. I had to wear thermal underwear and a fleece. I could only do one thing a day. I read myself wrong for ten years. And now I wasn't Dead Man. I was Third Man.

26)

It's not in a dream that I meet myself from ten years ago, the me from before the dead.

– Where were you? How come I let you go? I say.
– Where were *you*? the me from before says.

I wondered if this meeting would end in us melding together but I saw that I had changed, it wasn't possible. I hadn't really walked back to join myself, and I hadn't stood still.

– You were alive through all that, weren't you? the me from before says.
– Were you? I say.
– No, I wasn't, I say.

27)

'I saw you and I knew you as a bear
slow and round and then I saw you
again and you had become bony
and quick and I thought you had
got something; you were dying,
wasting away. But you're telling me
it was the bear that was ill?'

28)

I ran. I ran round Hackney Marshes,
I couldn't stop. I ran to see friends.
I ran away from home. I ran round in
circles. I ran. I ran myself down. I ran
down the road. I ran back. I ran backwards.
I ran to the end and ran back again. I ran
in the wrong direction. I ran into things.
I ran through everything. I ran out of
reasons. I ran a half marathon.

29)

I was sorry for what I had done and I was sorry for what I hadn't done. Now that I was who I had been (and not the person who had done and not done those things) I could go and see people I thought would want to hear me say that I was sorry for what I had done and not done. I could tell them that the reason why I had and had not done those things was to do with what I had become and not with who I was now. I could explain it all and say that I was sorry for what I had and had not done. So just as I planned, I made journeys to see the people who I thought would want to hear me say that I was sorry, truly and really sorry. They didn't.

He said, I am a misfortune bully,
I punch you with disasters.
I slap you in the face with the awful.
I'm a death junkie.
Feed me news about the dying.
Tell me about plague.
I need to know about the hidden poisons
that come in through the window
or stick in the cracks of broken plates.
Even leaning on your elbows is risky.
I come sniffing round your way
if I hear of someone who's copped it.
I'm the president of the fatal illness association
and I will be at your side
the moment I learn that
you or anyone you know is in a life-threatening situation.
You will think I'm here to help.

If you need cheering up
you should try to make other people miserable.
If you're finding it hard running your own life
you should try to run someone else's.
If you think you're doing someone wrong
you should tell them it's their fault.
If someone asks you a question and you don't want to answer it
you should draw their attention to the way they asked the
question.
If you are unhappy that you feel weaker than someone
you should lie to them.
If you feel unappreciated
you should pour contempt on those you think of as beneath
you.
If you feel you've lost touch with what's real
you should try to make people believe in things that you don't
believe in.
If you're not sure of the value of what you're doing
then you should denigrate what someone else is doing.
If you fear you've let someone down
you should tell them that they've let you down.
If you hate being grateful
you should do things that require other people to be grateful to
you.

If you feel that you're not needed
you should tell people that no one thanks you for what you've done for them.
If you're afraid of hearing what someone thinks of you
you should tell them what you think they think of you.
If you feel weak
you should tell people what you think their problem is.
If you feel guilty
you should tell other people that they're trying to do bad things to you.

When the Brits found out that they had lost Singapore, they wondered if the local population might come in handy when it came to making things awkward for the Japs. In Sun Yat-Sen House I saw an exhibition of documents from the time and one told how a couple of British colonels made contact with local Communists and asked them what they could do. Could they, for example, organize a general strike? There was a photo of them, two bony long-headed Brits, moustaches and Imperial shorts and Chinese guys standing to attention. I thought of them saying, I say, you men, any chance of a general strike?

It didn't take long for me to get the feel of a
Connecticut suburb. Each house set back
from the road but more public than in England.
No front fence or hedge, so bikes and wood are
on show. By looking down the sides of the houses,
you can even see the back lawn. Quite often the flag
is flying, people happy with who they are and where
they are, I supposed. I walked down to the deli
wondering how many of them were dentists when I
saw on one front lawn a torpedo, painted in red white
and blue. It lay there, pointing at the road, and down
the side someone had written: This one's for you,
Saddam.

The phone rang. It was three in the morning.
– Hello? We'll kill you, you fucking jew,
someone said and put the phone down. Perhaps
I've seen him in the street, or sat next to him
on the bus.

I was in an airport at three in the morning
and a man was selling flags: Australia,
Nigeria, Great Britain, Hong Honk.
– I said, Excuse me, I don't want to be
  rude, but shouldn't that say Hong Kong?
– It does say Hong Kong, he said.
– Well, actually, it says Hong Honk,
  I said.
– No, it doesn't, he said.
– Look, I said, I don't mind either way.
– Do you want the flag? he said.
– No, I don't, I said.
– Well there you are, he said.

They say that Sir Alex, when frustrated that a player was not performing at his best, stood an inch or two from the man's nose and yelled into his face. This, we are told, was called the 'hair-dryer treatment'. Lovers call it 'just trying to get you to understand'.

The female Remnaunt Spider copulates with two males alternately: first one, then the other, then back to the first, then back to the second, and so on. At some point, she halts the process with one of her mates and then, out of sight, in her den, she and the male that she still mates with eat the other male.

I was sleeping on my own, in the basement
with the house above me – one, two rooms
and an attic above my head and now no one
in the rooms, it had come to an end, and my
head was lying where a fireplace had been,
perhaps the room I was in was for a Victorian
servant to use, the rest had been a coal cellar.
Now it was a basement room. The fireplace
wasn't there, I was thinking, it had been taken
out. A builder had come and taken it out when
it was turned into a room. But in the room
above there was not only a fireplace but also
a great marble surround with a chimney breast
that went on up to the room above and then on,
up into the attic above that and as I lay there I
wondered what was holding it all up. Aren't
builders supposed to put girders or lintels or
beams across when they take out fireplaces
and I tried to remember if that builder had
brought in anything like that and I couldn't
remember that he had. Which would mean that
the whole chimney breast running up to the
roof was resting on, resting on what? The edge
of the floor above? The ceiling above my head?

But that would be a nothing. I got up and
went upstairs into the empty room above where
I had been lying and looked at the marble fireplace
and my eyes went up the chimney breast to the
ceiling and there was a small crack running from
the edge of the chimney breast at an angle across
the ceiling. And another one on the other side. I
ran upstairs again into the room above this one
and looked up to the ceiling. And there was
another pair of cracks there too. I had never seen
them before. But then I had never looked before.
Not once in the five years since the fireplace
was taken out. In all that time, when the house
had been full, all that jumping and larking about,
and I had never looked. So I rang a builder and
when he came over we went down into the
basement together and he knocked a hole in the
ceiling and put his hand through the hole. I'm
looking for a beam or a lintel, he said. Something
to hold the whole thing up. Nothing, he said. There's
nothing here. You feel. And I put my hand in the hole
and waved my hand about and he was right. In all that
time there had been nothing there to hold it all up.

I used to be bothered that cat food smells like shit. Now I'm bothered that my shit smells like cat food.

We haven't got long. I'd rather begin with
birth but death reminds me that what I'm
talking about comes to an end. Like when
we cross a bridge. The road might carry on
but at some point before that, you can
see that it's no longer a bridge. I take
from this that we're either on the bridge
or off it. I've noticed that some bridges
carry three-lane freeways, others no more
than a cow. Some have toll gates. You're
charged for being there. Sometimes they
collapse and a London bus once leapt
across the gap between the two halves of
Tower Bridge. One wobbled so much they
had to de-wobble it. They've been mined,
strafed and bombed. People we've never heard
of have jumped, though Horatio was used to
stir the blood of boys. There was a bridge
that was 'too far', meaning, I think, something
desperate. There's also a problem of how we
think about those who've crossed, those who've
got to the other end: only some are counted.

It was Carpet Madness at Carpet City in the Retail Park. We looked at vinyls and laminates. Most of them looked like something else – like tiles, wood, marble or granite. People seem to like that. Smooth hard plastic, looking like grainy wood or Italian kitchens. The Electricity showroom opposite us had rows of coal-effect fires and round the corner there was wallpaper that looked like stone walls. In the roads my friends lived in, there were houses with black strips of wood fixed on to the front walls. Their parents called them 'Tudor style'. And we had hundreds of small diamond panes in the windows of our flat. There are coaching lamps in our road that you couldn't put on a stagecoach. Outside the canteen today there was a plastic pie bigger than my head.

The obituary talked of his
pioneering activities in the
world of further education.
It didn't once mention that,
on a camp-site, when his
son and me were boys, he
could kill a wasp by pinching
its head. One squeeze.

They sold the school. It was developed. It became a place of apartments put up for sale by a firm called Artisans. The school wall has been kept so that it can be a gated estate. The old sign, SBL, the School Board of London, has been cleaned. It looks good. Nearby families get on buses looking for schools.

The cat's ignoring me.
So I'm ignoring the cat.
Which means I'm not.

They told us on the radio about men who had been killed in the Falklands. We heard from their families and I heard a daughter and her mother trying not to cry when they said how much they had loved the man. He was a computer freak, due home, but then re-directed to the Falklands, where he manned his computer while others got off on to their life rafts. I understood by that he was destroyed in the fire that swept through the boat. This woman, or perhaps it was another, said that she couldn't begin to think about whether it had all been worth it, but the interviewer was able to help out by explaining to her that her husband was protecting us. Dead men, families with dead men, the lives they wanted to lead twisted up. The defence of a far-off patch of British soil sounded so like a principle until we heard that on an island elsewhere in the old Empire, brown-skinned people had been shipped off to Mauritius, to make room for American runways.

Is this how it is? Two watchmakers
Oskar and Martin Rosen (or Rozen)
living, says their nephew Ted, in a
rue de Thionville in Metz or Nancy,
weren't there any more. Ted, now 94,
remembers his sister Olga practising
French by post and a letter from one
of the watchmakers arriving at their
home in Brockton, Mass. But after the
War, nothing. Is that how it is? A tank
or a bomb; a shell or a bullet removes
two people? Or does a group of men
turn up with a truck – then it's a depot,
a train, a camp; cholera, hunger or gas?
Is that how it is? Two watchmakers in
a street that's in the way. Then nothing.

These nothings make it all so easy
for people who give orders for war.
Perhaps Oskar and Martin appear in
the sum of French deaths. Unlikely – they
were born in Poland – a detail
which made them eligible for removal.
Perhaps they appear in the sum of

Polish deaths – unlikely – they had left.
Perhaps they are in the sum of Jewish
deaths – not necessarily, it depends
who was counting.

So that's how it is. You're a watchmaker,
then you're not. Tiny springs, tiny cogs,
Tick, tock, tick, tock, tick . . .

These shops, the flats over the shops and this cinema, all closed. Boarded up. Some for fifteen years, some for ten and five. Most of the road between here and the station. It was a station but they closed it. The bit of the line that was in the City was worth millions so they sold it off for offices. The council put charities in some of the shops. But they cut the funding so the charities closed. Then they pulled some of it down, built a block and opened it up as, they said, apartments and retail units. One of them someone opened as a party shop. A place that sells balloons and party poppers. One section the council took over as offices for Enterprise projects. 'We turn ideas into business . . .' We're waiting for a string of investors, the spokeswoman said. A string of investors to develop the area. Abdul from the Ganges tried to buy the one next to him so at least he could stop it flooding his restaurant. In the end, they said they would hold an auction. When they got there they said they wouldn't sell to people like Abdul, they wanted a string of investors. An outfit called Urban Spectrum bought the lot and put up signs on the boarded-up fronts, saying: To rent. When you ring, they say they're not for rent. They're waiting for the price to rise, so they can sell them off. Good business. So they're still empty. And falling down. When you go by on the bus, you can see into the flats. Pigeons flying in and out.

Some of them with the roofs off and you can see the flowers on the wallpaper. And the fireplaces that people used to sit round. Years go by. Nothing to do with us, said the spokeswoman, we sold them to an investor.

I said I lost him.

But I'm not the only one who lost him.
He belonged to others and he belonged to himself.

And it wasn't him I lost. He was who he was.
I lost whatever there was between us.

No, it isn't that I lost whatever there was
between us. Whatever there was between us
became something else.

No, it didn't become something else and then stop.
It became something else, and then something else,
and then something else again.

It became something that keeps becoming.

There was a joke he used to tell about a man who had an orange for his head. The man's head was an orange. That was the joke. The bit about the orange came at the end of the joke. You only found out that his head was an orange at the end. But I don't remember what the joke was. And that was a joke he used to tell. The man with an orange for his head. Then I found a version of it in a magazine. So I pinned it up on our board. But later we took the board down, and I lost the joke. I can't find it anywhere. I loved that joke. He loved it. But I can't find it. And I can't find anyone who knows it. It's gone. There was a joke and now there isn't a joke.

I am peeling an apple. A Bramley's.
Eight of them. They sit in the water
in the sink and as I pull the peeler
round, the shavings drop into the water.
By the time I lift the last apple out,
I have to shake it free of green skin
and dug-out black bits. The naked
apples sit in a colander on the draining
board, waiting for me to chop them into
eight segments on a board. I carve out
the semi-circles of core and pips.
Then as I hold the crescents of apple
over a saucepan, cutting chips by
pulling the knife towards my thumb,
I am my mother. Water in, till she can
see it, a handful of sultanas, a chunk of
dark sugar and a cinnamon stick. Stewed
apple, my brother eating it out of the
saucepan. My kids don't like it very
much. But you do, don't you? Especially
if I bung it in a crumble.

We make a baby.
The baby smiles.
We laugh:
the baby makes us.

We buy her toys
but she plays with shoes:
she makes herself.

Could I have imagined anything like
the sight of my father holding my
boy's hand, walking down the passage
and into the front room, to see a child
of mine in a coffin? Or the sight of you
and me sitting in the middle of the same
room, as this new baby shuffles her way
along the sofa's edge?

A family arrived and said that they had papers
to prove that his house was theirs.
– No, no, said the man, my people have always lived here.
My father, grandfather . . . and look in the garden,
my great-grandfather planted that.
– No, no, said the family, look at the documents.

There was a stack of them.

– Where do I start? said the man.
– No need to read the beginning, they said,
Turn to the page marked 'Promised Land'.
– Are they legal? he said. Who wrote them?
– God, they said, God wrote them, look,
here come His tanks.

The wind has blown all day, the bushes
in the garden trying to tear themselves
out of the ground. Your old blue chair
that looks like it's made out of straw
has stayed right where it is, its legs
stuck in the lawn, but the parasol and
the cats' dish have taken off and landed
in another country. We didn't want to go
out with Elsie, she might have taken
off too, or some lump – a dustbin, box or
branch – might have hit her. She's old enough
to know that she didn't like being where
she was, but not old enough to
know or say that going out might make
things better. So we stayed indoors
and ate old Dutch cake and pitta bread
until, long after dark, the bushes outside
gave up the struggle. We dressed up and
walked round the streets, Elsie holding
your hand, me pushing the empty buggy,
through drifts of leaves and cartons and
polythene bags. The buses sailed by looking
like cross-channel ferries doing the night
crossing, while Elsie put one foot in front

of the other. We tried to work out how long,
well, really, how short, it's all been, since we
met in these streets, and now look at us,
walking our little liebeskind over the paving
stones. Then we came home and in bed
said that we would make everyone sing
I'm a little teapot short and stout, at our
wedding.

30)

Popping these white
pills out of their silver
cocoons. Two a day
every day every year.
Seeping into my cells,
all day, doing what
your thyroid does
without any help.
There under the skin
of your neck, where it
slides over your throat.
That's unfrozen me
again.